CW00685641

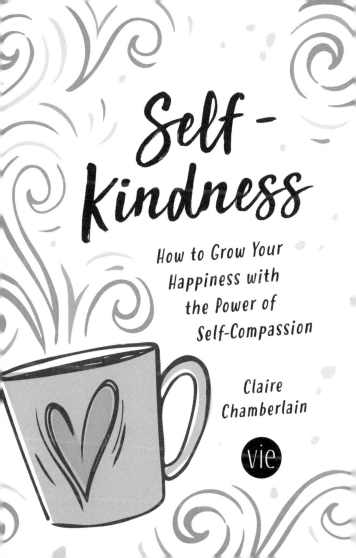

Self-Kindness

How to Grow Your Happiness with the Power of Self-Compassion

Claire
Chamberlain

vie

SELF-KINDNESS

An Hachette UK Company
www.hachette.co.uk

Vie Books, an imprint of Summersdale Publishers Ltd
Part of Octopus Publishing Group Limited
Carmelite House
50 Victoria Embankment
LONDON
EC4Y 0DZ
UK

www.summersdale.com

Printed and bound in Poland

ISBN: 978-1-80007-440-8

Substantial discounts on bulk quantities of Summersdale books are available to corporations, professional associations and other organizations. For details contact general enquiries: telephone: +44 (0) 1243 771107 or email: enquiries@summersdale.com.

Introduction

If you've noticed your internal dialogue is often negative, you never seem to have time for your own interests and passions, or you finish each day feeling run-down rather than relaxed, it might be time to introduce a little self-kindness into your life. Your mental and physical well-being depends on it. This book will help you get started, signposting the path toward care, compassion and kindness with its practical tips, inspiring quotes and uplifting affirmations – devoted just to you.

It's not selfish to *love* yourself,

take *care* of yourself,

and to make your *happiness*

a priority. It's *necessary*.

Mandy Hale

Get clear on self-kindness

Self-kindness is about treating yourself with care, taking the time to look after your own physical, mental and emotional needs. Everyday examples include eating well, getting some physical exercise, spending time in nature and scheduling adequate "downtime" in your day for rest and recuperation. Remember to be kind to yourself in the face of adversity, too. That includes, among other things, forgiving yourself for your past mistakes (we all make them).

Self-care is
not selfish. You
cannot serve
from an
empty vessel.

Eleanor Brown

WHY YOU
SHOULD PRACTISE
SELF-KINDNESS

Self-kindness is vital for your
well-being. You spend each and every
day with yourself, after all, so the way you
relate to yourself is bound to affect how
you feel. Research backs this up: scientists
have found that self-kindness plays a vital
role in mental well-being. One study even
found that self-kindness may impact our
physiology, improving both our immune
and behavioural responses. It's probably
time to start looking out for yourself.

YOU ARE
GOOD ENOUGH
EXACTLY AS
YOU ARE

I have met myself
and I am going to care
for her fiercely.

Glennon Doyle

Self-kindness and mental well-being

It makes sense that being kind to yourself is going to make you feel calmer and happier, but the evidence for this is not merely anecdotal: research shows that practising kindness (including toward yourself) boosts the levels of serotonin and dopamine (the happiness hormones) in your brain. One survey found that 48 per cent of its 4,246 adult participants agreed that being kind to themselves had a positive impact on their mental health. This means that practising self-kindness, though naturally beneficial to us all, is especially important if you sometimes struggle with your mental health. That's because anxiety, depression and other mental health problems can signal a serotonin deficiency. What might self-kindness look like for you today? Perhaps it's giving yourself half an hour to delve into a favourite book or making peace with something or someone in your past.

LOVE YOURSELF ENOUGH
TO SET BOUNDARIES.
YOUR TIME AND ENERGY
ARE PRECIOUS.
YOU GET TO CHOOSE
HOW YOU USE IT.

ANNA TAYLOR

ALL YOUR
FEELINGS
ARE VALID,
NOT JUST THE
POSITIVE ONES

BE GENTLE
WITH
YOURSELF
TODAY

We need to do a
better job of putting
ourselves higher on
our own "to do" list.

Michelle Obama

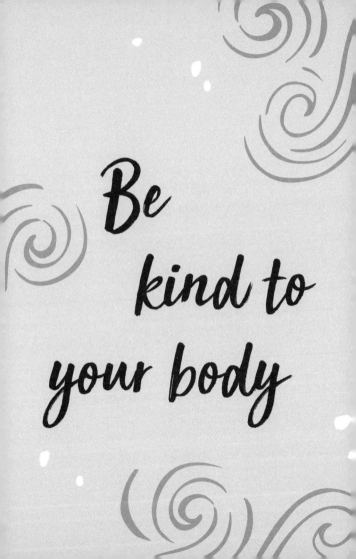

Treating yourself with compassion and kindness not only offers mental health benefits, but can boost your physical health, too. Stress, for example, can play havoc with your body – and left unchecked it can contribute to a number of health problems, including heart disease and diabetes. But studies have shown that treating yourself with compassion, particularly through practices such as mindfulness, can be highly beneficial when it comes to stress relief. Reducing your stress levels with self-kindness practices can result in lower blood pressure, improved circulation, a lower heart rate and even boost your immunity. And the benefits don't end there: by consciously being kinder to yourself, you're more likely to implement healthier long-term habits for your body, such as making sure you're drinking enough water or taking the stairs instead of the elevator. How might you be a little kinder to your body today?

LEARNING TO LOVE YOURSELF IS LIKE LEARNING TO WALK — ESSENTIAL, LIFE-CHANGING AND THE ONLY WAY TO STAND TALL.

VIRONIKA TUGALEVA

Boost your self-esteem

It makes sense that there's a well-recognized link between self-kindness and self-esteem. If you begin to value yourself enough to treat yourself with compassion, carve out enough space in each and every day for your own needs, forgive your past mistakes and cultivate more joy and happiness in your life, then your sense of self-worth is going to soar. So, if you're struggling with self-esteem and confidence right now, a little self-kindness could turn things around.

YOU ARE
WORTHY OF
LOVE AND
HAPPINESS

Once you choose hope,
anything is possible.

Christopher Reeve

Barriers to self-kindness

Being kinder to yourself sounds simple, right? And of course, it is... on the surface. However, once you start trying to implement a little more self-kindness into your daily life, you might find that you come across a few obstacles that refuse to budge. These barriers to self-kindness can be broken down into two broad categories: physical barriers (those outside of yourself) and mental barriers (the barriers you impose upon

yourself). Examples of common physical barriers include lack of time and lack of support (such as childcare). Mental barriers include feelings of guilt for spending time caring for yourself, a belief that you should constantly put the needs of your dependants before your own, and that you are not deserving of self-kindness or compassion. We'll explore some of these barriers in more detail in the pages that follow.

I have come to
believe that caring for
myself is not indulgent.
Caring for myself is
an act of survival.

Audre Lorde

IT'S NOT SELFISH TO PUT YOURSELF FIRST SOMETIMES

Make time for self-kindness

What with work, responsibilities and chores, you may feel that you don't have time to care for yourself. But self-kindness doesn't have to be lengthy. Far from it. Sometimes self-kindness is simply about changing the way you view yourself. Of course, things like practising meditation need a little time, but even 10 minutes is often enough. Scheduling self-kindness by writing it as an appointment in a journal can help you to stick to a routine.

Be your own best friend

Take a moment to think about the qualities of a good friend: perhaps they are understanding, comfort you when you feel low, buoy you up when you've had a bad day and are your biggest cheerleader when you try something new. Now ask yourself: Do you treat yourself in this way? Do you always have your own back? If not, perhaps it's time to become your own best friend.

Self-compassion is simply *giving*

the same ***kindness*** to ourselves

that we would ***give*** to others.

Christopher Germer

Nurturing your
self-compassion is
anti-oppression work
within yourself.

Joy Donnell

Know it's OK to ask for help

Sometimes you may need to enlist support in order to look after yourself effectively. There's never any shame in asking for support, especially if this will be the difference between strengthening your inner reserves and burning out. Make sure your loved ones are on side to step in when you need time to rest and reset.

SPEAK
KINDLY TO
YOURSELF,
ALWAYS

If your compassion
does not include yourself,
it is incomplete.

Jack Kornfield

DROP THE GUILT

Often, one of the biggest mental barriers to
self-compassion is guilt; after all, many of us live
in a culture that's conditioned us to believe that
being constantly busy is the key to success. On top
of that, you may feel that spending time tending to
your own needs is somehow selfish. But remember,
looking after your own well-being will ultimately
leave you with more energy for others, not
less. It's time to drop the guilt and recognize
self-kindness as necessary and vital.

LIGHTEN UP ON YOURSELF.
NO ONE IS PERFECT.
GENTLY ACCEPT YOUR
HUMANNESS.

DEBORAH DAY

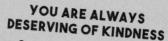

YOU ARE ALWAYS
DESERVING OF KINDNESS

Some days, it's easy to treat
yourself with kindness and
compassion – days when you've
done something well and received
praise from others, for example.
But other times, perhaps when
you've made a mistake, feel like
you have let someone down, or
feel like you failed, it can leave
you feeling guilty. But let's get
something clear: no matter your
mood, achievements or the
external circumstances, you are
always deserving of kindness,
and self-kindness is a
vital starting point.

Put yourself first

The majority of us are not used to putting ourselves first. We've often been conditioned to believe that such an act is selfish. Then there are all those important commitments in our lives – families, work, friends. It's easy to find yourself slipping down your own priorities list. But it's time to address this. Begin by giving yourself permission to care about yourself, by reminding yourself that your own mental, physical and emotional well-being is an absolute must.

Remember that being kind to yourself – through your words, actions and deeds – is imperative for your confidence, self-esteem and happiness. It's not only OK to bump yourself a little higher up your own to-do list: it's wholly necessary. So, you've vowed to put yourself first more often. Now what? The tips that follow serve as a guide to help you put your well-being pledge into action.

Cultivating self-kindness

Once you've decided to embark on the radical journey of self-kindness, where do you start? Because it isn't all about warm, candlelit baths and face masks (although these can definitely form a part of it). True self-kindness is about diving more deeply within yourself. It's about dismantling old, unhelpful habits (such as automatic negative self-talk and people pleasing) and replacing these with new ways of thinking. It's about assessing and ridding yourself of behaviours that are damaging your mental health, and creating new, empowering behavioural patterns that serve to strengthen your mindset and bring you more joy, happiness and peace. It's about getting comfortable with saying "no" to others, in order to make space for your own passions and projects. In short, it's about caring for yourself deeply, not just superficially.

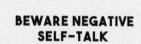

BEWARE NEGATIVE SELF-TALK

When that little voice inside your head pipes up, what does it say? If you're used to telling yourself, "I'm useless," it's time to nip that negative self-talk in the bud. Next time your inner monologue turns mean, replace it immediately with a more positive thought. For example, "I'm such a failure," could become, "That didn't go to plan, but I've learned from the experience, so next time will be better." Be kind and constructive.

The happiness of your
life depends upon the
quality of your thoughts.

Marcus Aurelius

Talk to yourself
like you would to
someone you love.

Brené Brown

ACCEPT
YOURSELF
FULLY,
EXACTLY
AS YOU ARE

Don't look for happiness in other people, find it in yourself.

Katie Piper

BE
WONDERFULLY
AND
UNIQUELY
YOU

Learn to say "no"

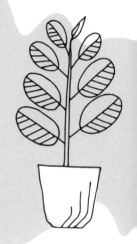

How often do you say "yes" without considering your own commitments or mental well-being first? The sad fact is that in an effort to seem amenable, many of us shoulder additional responsibilities before even questioning whether we want to take them on. "No" doesn't have to be rude: a simple, "Thanks for asking, but I'm afraid I don't have space for that right now," is a firm but polite response, leaving you feeling empowered and with more time on your hands for you.

When you are saying "*yes*"

to others, make sure you are

not saying "*no*" to yourself.

Paulo Coelho

Forgive yourself fully

Everybody makes mistakes sometimes – they're a natural part of human development. So, when things go wrong, don't be hard on yourself. Of course, it's important to be accountable and take ownership of bad judgements or decisions; but moving on, rather than dwelling, is crucial for your mental health. Accept what has happened, apologize if necessary, and then forgive yourself fully. Learning from your mistakes and moving forward is a far healthier pattern to adopt than getting stuck in a cycle of guilt.

HAVING COMPASSION
STARTS AND ENDS WITH
HAVING COMPASSION FOR
ALL THOSE UNWANTED
PARTS OF OURSELVES.

PEMA CHÖDRÖN

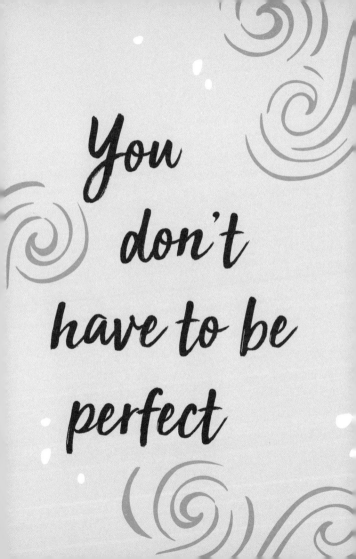

As Elizabeth Gilbert once said, "Perfectionism is just fear in fancy shoes and a mink coat." And it's true. Think about it: how many times have you given up on something before you've even started, for fear of falling short of your own benchmark of perfection? It could be a creative project, a job application, a relationship… You're being unkind to yourself when you aim for unrealistically high standards. Perfection sets you up to fail, often at the cost of trying new and exciting endeavours – endeavours that might bring you so much joy if only you'd let yourself give them a go. Letting go of perfection is one of the ultimate expressions of self-kindness. Realizing that "good enough" truly is exactly that allows you to throw yourself into new hobbies, projects, relationships and friendships, and really live life to the full without fear of failure. All you have to do is to try your best – because that really is good enough.

I've finally stopped running away from myself. Who else is there better to be?

Goldie Hawn

FORGIVE YOUR PAST MISTAKES — WE ALL MAKE THEM

Watch your language

Sometimes, something as simple as altering your vocabulary can see you treating yourself more gently and with greater compassion. Think about those times when you felt like a ton of responsibilities and chores were weighing down on you: changing your language from "should" to "could" in these instances can help to take some of the pressure off. For example, telling yourself you "should" clear your inbox or get that laundry put away is very different from telling yourself

you "could" clear your inbox or get that laundry put away. "Should" is laden with judgement: you're a bad person if you don't get this done. Whereas "could" helps to lift the guilt: you could get these chores done, but if you don't quite get around to it, then it doesn't matter. Using language that gives you a little breathing space and flexibility, rather than using terms that imply a rigid framework that must be adhered to, means you're being far kinder to yourself.

Self-care means
giving yourself
permission to pause.

Cecilia Tran

I've been searching for
ways to heal myself,
and I've found that
kindness is the best way.

Lady Gaga

Practise gratitude

Gratitude is the perfect companion to self-kindness.
It helps you to notice, experience and feel thankful
for the good things in your life, however small or
seemingly insignificant. Feeling grateful can give
you a big boost in the well-being stakes. Studies
have found that gratitude can help you feel more
fulfilled, increase your self-esteem and improve
your overall mental well-being. But how? According
to scientists, we humans are generally predisposed
to notice the negative events in our lives.

But by actively drawing our attention to the good things, we begin to reinforce our "positive memory bias", meaning the more we feel grateful for, the more we naturally begin to notice the positives in life. Try writing down three things you feel grateful for at the end of each day (it could be something as simple as the hot cup of tea you enjoyed) and see how quickly this self-kindness habit improves your outlook on life.

DO MORE
THINGS THAT
FILL YOU
WITH JOY

YOU ARE WORTHY OF
LOVE AND RESPECT.
YOU ARE BEAUTIFUL,
GIFTED AND INTELLIGENT.
DON'T LET THE STORM
MAKE YOU FORGET IT.

RUSSELL T. DAVIES

Write it down

If you often feel like you have a tangle of thoughts in your head, which is making you feel stressed, journalling might help you feel calmer. Most of us aren't in the habit of writing down our innermost thoughts and feelings regularly, so you may feel uncomfortable at first. However, many people swear by journalling as a way of making sense of their emotions, as well as allowing them the space to gain clarity and perspective. You don't need anything fancy to start – just a pen and notebook, and you're good to go. If writing long paragraphs isn't your thing, or if you don't have a lot of time, even jotting down bullet points can be cathartic. You can note down anything and everything, from things that have happened in your day to your thoughts, emotions and feelings. Once you get into the habit, journalling can be a simple self-kindness habit for making sense of your world.

Pause, reflect, reset

We're all prone to falling into habits that can become so automatic, they feel like they're set in stone. It's important to remember that they aren't. Think about what is (and isn't) working in your life. What makes you feel joyful? How might you incorporate more of this into each day? What isn't working? How could you resolve these issues? In short, figure out how you could streamline your life to make it work better for you.

WE CAN BE MORE OF
THE PERSON WE KNOW
IS POSSIBLE WHEN WE
GET IN THE HABIT OF
SELF-KINDNESS.

TARA BRACH

ENGAGE WITH MINDFULNESS

Mindfulness simply means being fully aware of the present moment, exactly as it is, without judgement. Being fully present encourages you to experience each moment more deeply, heightening your sense of fulfilment and relaxation. If you're often lost in your thoughts, caught in a never-ending loop of worries, then mindfulness could help. Start by practising this wonderful act of self-kindness for just 5 to 10 minutes each day – and be gentle with yourself if you find at first you get a little distracted. An easy way to start is to spend a little time focusing your attention on each of your senses in turn: what can you see, hear, smell, feel... even taste?

BREATHE
IN SLOWLY,
EXHALE
DEEPLY

Switch off

Being constantly tuned in to the online world (especially social media and the news) does your mental health no favours. But you don't have to ditch the tech completely. A 2018 study found that reducing time spent on social media to 30 minutes a day resulted in a significant reduction in anxiety, depression, loneliness, sleep problems and fear of missing out (FOMO). Try switching your phone to silent and keeping it out of your sight every now and then – it could do wonders for your well-being.

Almost everything
will work again if
you unplug it
for a few minutes,
including you.

Anne Lamott

Accept yourself fully

True self-kindness means accepting yourself completely, "flaws" and all. It's not only about loving yourself when your hair looks good, when you've achieved a goal or when things are going well in life. It's also about accepting and embracing the wonderful, messy, gloriously flawed, whole human being that you are, in both the good times and the bad. Because only when self-kindness is unerring is it truly complete.

PLEDGE THAT YOU WILL
LOOK IN THE MIRROR
AND FIND THE UNIQUE
BEAUTY IN YOU.

TYRA BANKS

Don't compare yourself to others

We live in an era in which people seem to document everything online – from their dinners to their holiday destinations. It can feel like harmless fun swiping through other people's lives online. But be careful not to get caught up in the joy-sapping habit of comparison, measuring yourself against other people's heavily curated highlights. Remember, no one's life is as perfect as it might seem – you're only being shown a snapshot – and yours probably measures up just fine.

COMPARISON IS AN ACT OF VIOLENCE AGAINST THE SELF.

IYANLA VANZANT

REFRAME FAILURE

Always remember: failure is not final.
It's not a sign that you're a bad person or
that you're incapable. It's a sign that you've
tried something new. It's a sign that you've been
brave. Every time you fail at something you
learn in the process, and if you embrace your
own resilience, dust yourself off and give it
another go, you might get a little further
next time. So, go on, allow yourself to
try and fail – it's how we grow.

Sometimes, you have to fall to the ***bottom*** in order to make your way back to the ***top*** again.

Bryony Gordon

Find out
who you are
and do it
on purpose.

Dolly Parton

Celebrate your strengths

Take a moment to consider your strengths (remember, this isn't just about acknowledging "specific" achievements). For instance, are you kind, empathetic, organized, creative, enthusiastic, resourceful, resilient? Never hide the qualities that make you uniquely you. Instead, be proud of who you are and really own your strengths. After all, being your own cheerleader and celebrating the things that make you shine is a vital act of self-kindness.

DO SOMETHING THAT NOURISHES YOUR SOUL

Joy does not simply happen to us. We have to choose joy and keep choosing it every day.

Henri Nouwen

Do more
of what
makes
you happy

We all have tasks, chores, work and life admin to complete each day. But what are you doing with the rest of your time? Some days, your free time might seem fleeting or marginal, but be sure to spend it doing something you love. Create a list of all the things you enjoy. The list can be wide ranging – things like taking a warm shower, drinking a cup of tea, reading a novel, journalling, painting, sketching, listening to music, dancing, going for a walk, learning a new skill... if it brings you happiness, add it to your list. Then try to include as many of these joyful things into each day as you can, even if for a few minutes. Filling your day with things that make you happy is a wonderful act of kindness and can turn your whole outlook around.

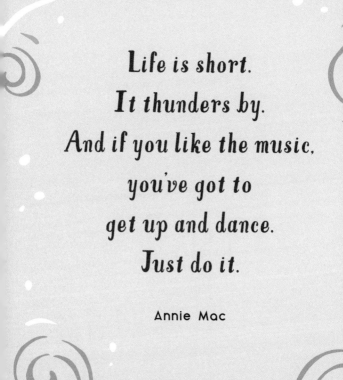

Life is short.
It thunders by.
And if you like the music,
you've got to
get up and dance.
Just do it.

Annie Mac

LIVE FULLY,
FEEL DEEPLY

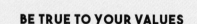

BE TRUE TO YOUR VALUES

What are your core values, the qualities
that are most important to you? Ensuring
that you live fully in accordance with these
values is going to see you feeling more
content and connected, and ultimately
living a more enriched life. Making sure
that you are upholding and honouring your
values as you go through each day is an
important way of living authentically, of
showing yourself compassion and kindness.

Make a list of what is
really important to you.
Embody it.

Jon Kabat-Zinn

NO ONE WILL
UNDERSTAND YOU.
IT IS NOT, ULTIMATELY,
THAT IMPORTANT.
WHAT IS IMPORTANT
IS THAT YOU
UNDERSTAND YOU.

MATT HAIG

TRUST YOUR INSTINCTS: YOU KNOW WHAT'S BEST FOR YOU

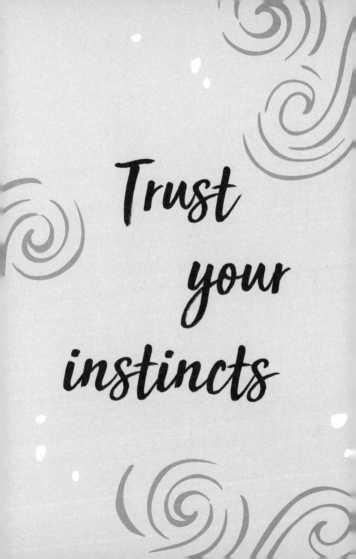

If, deep down, something isn't sitting well with you, it's probably not right for you and may even be doing you harm. Burying your head in the sand – perhaps due to a bad relationship or toxic friendship – might seem like a good way of protecting yourself, but it will only cause you pain in the long run (if it hasn't done so already). Being honest with yourself is vital for your own peace of mind. If a situation or relationship instinctively feels wrong to you, then it probably is, and any sugar-coating is only going to see the situation eat away at you inside, stealing your inner peace and disrupting everything from your sleep to your eating habits. It can seem scary at first, but being honest with yourself – and those around you – is always the best way forward. Be brave. Speak your truth. Be open with yourself and others, and trust in the validity of your feelings.

Loving other people

starts with loving ourselves

and **accepting** ourselves.

Elliot Page

FOCUS ON ALL THAT YOU ARE, INSTEAD OF ALL THAT YOU ARE NOT

Listen to your body

Work stress, late nights out with friends, too much alcohol, days on end consuming nothing but junk food and caffeine... let's face it, we have all been there. If you put your body through a lot from time to time, you're definitely not alone. But when your body starts sending you signals telling you it needs a break, do you listen? Signs that you might have been burning the candle at both ends for a little too long include feelings of tiredness (or downright exhaustion),

skin changes, tummy troubles (such as bloating or constipation), aches and pains, low mood and difficulty concentrating. Pushing on through is only going to make matters worse. Pause and recharge. Do what you can to make some space for yourself, however much you've got going on in your life. Get a few early nights, eat some wholesome foods, lay off the booze, drink plenty of water, stretch, meditate, rest. Accept that sometimes, your body knows best.

KINDNESS
IS NOT
WEAKNESS

True happiness
and true power lie
in understanding
yourself, accepting
yourself, having
confidence in
yourself.

Thích Nhất Hạnh

Remember:
it's not all or nothing

Making some small, positive lifestyle changes is a great step toward supporting mind and body health. It could be that you decide to walk short distances instead of driving, swap sugary desserts for fruit, or vow to have meat-free meals a few days a week. Just remember that when it comes to exercise, healthy eating or anything else in life, you haven't "failed" if you fall off the wagon every now and then.

It's never all or nothing. Slipping back into old habits for a day (or even a week) doesn't mean it is time to give up completely. So, as a huge act of self-kindness, stop beating yourself up for not sticking to healthy living plans rigidly. Flexibility, as always, is the key to happiness (and to kindness).

BE HEALTHY AND TAKE
CARE OF YOURSELF,
BUT BE HAPPY WITH THE
BEAUTIFUL THINGS THAT
MAKE YOU, YOU.

BEYONCÉ

Make some healthy food swaps

Being kind to your body doesn't mean going on a juice diet that leaves you starving by lunchtime on day one. Making a series of small changes is actually better for your body, as it's a more sustainable approach. One way to start is by making some healthy food swaps. Try herbal tea instead of your morning latte or snack on plain popcorn instead of crisps. Lifestyle changes don't have to be drastic to have a positive impact.

IT'S BETTER TO TRY THAN TO NEVER EVEN START

Every small, positive
change we make in ourselves
repays us in confidence
in the future.

Alice Walker

The effects of alcohol

While many of us enjoy the odd tipple or two, it's important to remember that – despite the feelings of relaxation those first few sips induce – alcohol is a depressant. This means that if you are drinking often, or in large quantities, it's going to have some negative effects on both your body and mind. These can include heightened anxiety (especially when feeling hung-over), disrupted sleep patterns and fatigue, with longer-term effects including liver problems and an increased risk of some cancers. Remember, alcohol is addictive. If you've begun to turn to alcohol in moments of stress, it can easily become an unhealthy coping mechanism. To be truly kind to yourself is to be totally honest about your relationship with alcohol. Start by asking yourself whether there's a need for you to cut back. We would all benefit from sticking to the weekly recommendations of 14 units of alcohol (roughly six medium glasses of wine or six pints of lager) or less, with at least two consecutive alcohol-free days a week.

You've been criticizing
yourself for years
and it hasn't worked.
Try approving of yourself
and see what happens.

Louise Hay

Self-care is how you
take your power back.

Lalah Delia

(Re)connect with nature

Spending time in the natural world is good for the soul. That's what one recent study found. Apparently, people who spend more time surrounded by nature look more kindly upon themselves. This is because doing so mutes our internal self-criticism or provides us with some "cognitive quiet", which in turn fosters a sense of self-compassion. Even if for a moment, try walking barefoot on the grass, taking your lunch break

in a local park or pausing and listening to birdsong. If you have a little longer, why not give *shinrin-yoku* (forest-bathing) a go? The practice involves immersing yourself in the sights, sounds and scents of a natural environment – a forest, woodland, meadow or shoreline, perhaps – by really slowing down and absorbing the calming surroundings. It's time to show yourself a little love and kindness and venture outside.

GET LOST IN
NATURE —
YOU MIGHT
FIND YOURSELF

In every walk with
nature one receives far
more than he seeks.

John Muir

Move

more

We're leading increasingly sedentary lifestyles, which is doing nothing for our physical or mental health. So, make it your mantra to get up and move more each day. If you're worried about how you're going to squeeze fitness into your already jam-packed day, remember: exercise doesn't have to be a long-drawn-out process. Simply making it a habit to get more steps in each day is a great start; you could do this by setting an alarm on your phone to remind yourself to get up and walk around for 5 minutes every hour. You might decide to walk part of the way to work (or walk the kids to school instead of driving or taking the bus). Set yourself the challenge of doing ten squats every time you boil the kettle for a cup of tea. Blast the radio and dance around the kitchen. Just do anything you can think of to get moving and get those feel-good endorphins flowing.

No **day** is so bad

it can't be ***fixed*** with a nap.

Carrie Snow

Take a nap

It's official: researchers say napping is good for us. As well as reducing sleepiness, a nap can help boost concentration and memory recall, as well as improve alertness. A 30-minute nap will see you enter a deep, slow-wave sleep (the restorative kind, during which your body repairs and regenerates). If you don't have that much time, even a power nap of 20 minutes is beneficial. Just show yourself a little love by snuggling under a cozy duvet for a midday recharge.

Swap screen time for a good book before bed

It can be so easy, especially after a busy day, to sink into the sofa and mindlessly scroll through your phone, without even noticing the hours passing you by. While interacting with others online can give you a hit of dopamine (a neurotransmitter linked to an improvement in mood), compulsive scrolling before bed is a surefire way to keep your brain on high alert, inhibiting your ability to fall asleep.

Instead of reaching for your phone, try getting stuck into a good book. Reading before bed has been shown to reduce levels of cortisol (your body's main stress hormone). It acts as a buffer between your sleep time and the stresses you may have encountered during the day, too. And it will make your night's sleep more restful. Opt for an old-fashioned physical book to avoid the sleep-disruptive artificial blue-screen light emitted by electronic devices. It will be far kinder on your mind (and body) than a late-night social media session.

YOU HAVE
THE POWER
TO FORGE YOUR
OWN PATH

Invest in yourself

It's sometimes hard to justify splashing out on the cost of a new hobby – even more so as you get older and feel comfortably stuck in the groove of your usual routine. But doing something new is good for you, and it needn't cost anything. So what are you waiting for? Join a sports team. Take up yoga. Set up a book club. Go walking with friends. Whatever speaks to you, whatever feeds your soul – go for it. Because you are worth it.

What our families,
our companies, and
the world needs is
nothing more — and
nothing less — than
exactly who we are.

Abby Wambach

Always, always, always
believe in yourself,
because if you don't,
then who will?

Marilyn Monroe

Harness positive thinking

Positive self-talk is a wonderful way to be kind to yourself and can cancel out any negativity or limiting beliefs that might be hanging around in your mind. The key to affirmations is in repetition. If you repeat positive statements often enough, they will become beliefs, and believing them can have a profoundly positive impact on your life. Affirmations should be meaningful to you – choose something you want to start believing about yourself, or that reflects the life you wish to lead. It should be short and impactful. Something like, "I am fearless and free," "I am perfect exactly as I am," "I live mindfully in each moment," "I am beautiful and unique." Repeat your affirmation several times a day or write it on sticky notes that you can leave dotted around your room or house. Who knows how your life might change for the better because of it?

Embrace your creative side

Don't think you're creative? Think again. As humans, we are hardwired for creativity. It's how we've survived and thrived. Tapping into your creative side is essential for self-expression (and therefore self-understanding and self-compassion). Don't think too much about the end result – the joy is in the creative process. So, pick up a pen, pencil or paintbrush, and get writing, sketching, doodling, painting (or building, sculpting, playing, moving... it's entirely your call).

Treat
yourself

Everybody knows that buying a little impromptu gift for someone you love will light up their soul, making them feel loved, cared for and special. So, as you are practising self-kindness a little more, why not do the same for yourself? It doesn't have to be in any way expensive or extravagant. When you're out and about, why not pick up a second-hand book, a bright bunch of flowers or your favourite coffee from a local café? Not in the mood to cook dinner? Then ditch the pots and pans and order your favourite feel-good takeaway. If you're more about experiences, less about "things", you might treat yourself to a massage, manicure, reflexology session, or even just an hour of doing whatever you please without worrying about other people or productivity. Treating yourself is a wonderful way to honour and value yourself.

WE ALL
NEED TO
PRESS PAUSE
SOMETIMES

Within you, there is a
stillness and a sanctuary to
which you can retreat at any
time and be yourself.

Hermann Hesse

Try short, daily meditations

Performing a short daily meditation is a wonderfully calming self-kindness ritual. In fact, some studies have found that it can have powerful positive effects on both your body and mind, including lowering your heart rate and blood pressure, improving circulation and reducing stress. There are many different ways you can meditate. You might choose to follow your breath, focusing on each inhalation and exhalation to a count of ten before repeating. You could focus

instead on an external object, such as a candle flame or crystal. All meditation is simply focused attention. To begin, sit comfortably, with your back straight and upright; gently close your eyes, if you wish. Whichever way you decide to meditate, attempt to clear your mind of everything else. If thoughts creep in, gently draw your attention back, without judgement or guilt. Aim for just 5 to 10 minutes at a set time each day, if you can, maybe before you go to bed.

Create a soothing bedtime routine

In an ideal world, we'd all have time to relax properly before going to bed, creating the optimum mindset for a restful night's sleep. Often, however, we tend to have so much to cram into each day that we end up working or completing household chores right up until we brush our teeth. Sadly, attempting to fill every single hour of the day means we leave little room for much-needed headspace.

So, whenever possible (but preferably daily), try to carve out at least 30 minutes before bed to gently decelerate from your day. You might decide to use this time to read, take a bath, do some gentle stretching or perform a breathing meditation. The aim simply is to dedicate some time to yourself (because you deserve it), to slow your thoughts in preparation for sleep. And getting into the habit of enjoying some relaxing downtime will help signal to your body that it's time for sleep.

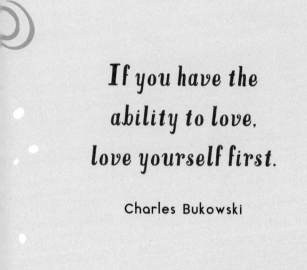

If you have the
ability to love,
love yourself first.

Charles Bukowski

YOU'RE
THE BEST AT
BEING YOU

Sleep well

Getting enough sleep each night is important for your overall well-being. During sleep, your body rejuvenates and repairs physically, leaving you feeling mentally calm and alert the following day. Guidelines recommend that, as adults, we need roughly 8 hours of sleep each night, although you may need to spend a little longer in bed in order to achieve this. To better aid a good night's sleep, make sure your bedroom environment is just right by maintaining a room temperature of 16–18°C; ensuring it's dark (try a blackout blind or eye mask if street lighting is a problem); making sure your mattress is firm but comfortable and by keeping noise to a minimum (ear plugs can be a lifesaver if you happen to live in an area where there are frequent disruptions, such as traffic noise). Doing yourself this kindness will help to set you up for the day ahead.

WAKE UP,
LIVE YOUR LIFE AND
SING THE MELODY
OF YOUR SOUL.

AMIT RAY

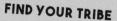

FIND YOUR TRIBE

Surrounding yourself with people who really get you – your values, passions, humour – will give you the chance to be authentically you. These people will be your cheerleaders. To find them, think about the people in your life who lift you up – the ones who seem to understand you at your very core – and make a conscious effort to spend more time with them. Conversely, it's time to remove the toxic people (those who bring you down) from your life. Actively cultivating your tribe in this way is an act of true self-kindness.

Surround yourself with
only people who are
going to lift you higher.

Oprah Winfrey

A problem shared...

If there is something on your mind – a worry or fear, for example – opening up can be a powerful act of self-kindness. Sharing your feelings can help to alleviate your anxiety due to the cathartic nature of talking through problems – feeling heard can be empowering. It doesn't need to be a face-to-face chat: messaging a friend is a great way to open up. Or if you want anonymity, chat forums on trusted mental health websites are a great way to enlist support.

DON'T LET FEAR ROB YOU OF YOUR HAPPINESS

TRUE FRIENDS
ARE LIKE DIAMONDS —
BRIGHT, BEAUTIFUL,
VALUABLE, AND
ALWAYS IN STYLE.

NICOLE RICHIE

Connect with your community

It's important to acknowledge the role that human connection plays when you're looking to be kinder to yourself. Start building a sense of community around yourself by chatting to neighbours, checking out community events, volunteering for a local project, borrowing a friend's dog to walk (if you don't have your own!) and chatting with other walkers... whatever works for you. We're social beings after all, and loneliness can have a profound effect on our well-being.

When we give ourselves
compassion, we are opening
our hearts in a way that can
transform our lives.

Kristin Neff

Spend time giving back

Doing good deeds can help those around you, as well as giving you a wonderful sense of purpose and connection. How will you positively affect others today? There are so many ways you can make a positive impact, from donating to a cause close to your heart, to smiling at a stranger, to paying someone a genuine compliment. Every little act of kindness in the world helps to cultivate happiness and positivity.

As you **grow** older, you will

discover that you have two

hands — one for **helping** yourself,

the other for helping **others**.

Audrey Hepburn

Ask for support

There are so many reasons why we might begin to feel overwhelmed in life (from a mental health problem to exam stress, an overload of tasks at work to a lack of help with childcare). Often we're left feeling alone and frustrated, assuming others will know how we feel. But unless we're brave enough to voice our feelings and ask for support, then those around us might never know how we really feel: that, deep down, we can't cope. Asking for help can be scary, but it's an important self-care step. First, figure out exactly what's making you feel overwhelmed. Then decide who would be the best person to talk to (perhaps a friend or family member, a healthcare professional, maybe even a colleague). Just try to be specific. Creating a strategy can be useful when it comes to getting the help you need. Sometimes being kind to yourself means accepting your own limitations and being vulnerable.

Love yourself first,
and everything
else falls in line.
You really have
to love yourself to
get anything done
in this world.

Lucille Ball

WHEN YOU'RE OVERWHELMED, IT'S OK TO ASK FOR SUPPORT

ASKING FOR
HELP DOESN'T
MAKE YOU
WEAK;
IT MAKES YOU
HUMAN

WHAT TO DO IF
YOU'RE STRUGGLING

If anxious, low thoughts are beginning
to overwhelm you, or you think you may
be struggling with more serious mental health
issues, it's important to reach out for help. If
opening up to a friend or family member feels too
difficult, or if you feel like you would benefit from
expert help, make an appointment with a medical
professional. There, you will be able to talk
openly in a safe, confidential space. Admitting
you need support can seem daunting,
but making that appointment is an
important act of self-kindness.

Each day offers a
reason to celebrate.
Find it and experience
true bliss.

Amy Leigh Mercree

We just need to be kinder to ourselves. If we treated ourselves the way we treated our best friend, can you imagine how much better off we would be?

Meghan, Duchess of Sussex

Live for yourself – not for others

Sometimes it feels as though doing things to make other people happy is the right way to go. We all want to make the people in our lives proud, right? Yet, this need to please or conform can have some serious negative consequences, especially if it sees you following someone else's path in life, rather than your own. Squeezing yourself to fit within the parameters of other people's expectations is only going to leave you feeling frustrated, limited, as if the

life you're living is a bit, well... small. It's time to think
(and live) BIG. What do you dream of doing or being?
What could you achieve if you stepped outside
other people's boundaries? What do you value
most in life and how might you live in accordance
with that? Shaking off other people's expectations,
following your own path and living according to
your values, is the ultimate act of self-kindness.
How will you start living for yourself today?

YOU'VE
GOT THIS

Conclusion

We all have days when we forget the importance of showing ourselves some kindness. But if those days drag into weeks, or even months, it can leave us feeling low. Whether it's changing the way you speak to yourself or performing a small act of self-care, showing yourself kindness each day can help you feel more positive and empowered. Now's the time to start investing more energy into the most important relationship in your life – the one you have with yourself.

SELF-CARE

Claire Chamberlain

Hardback

978-1-78685-775-0

Self-care is the essential action of looking after your mind, body and soul. Dip into this book whenever your energy is flagging and choose one of its many quick and easy self-care tips, from gaining strength with invigorating walks and delicious, healthy food to treating yourself to a slow evening of face masks and hot soaks. This soothing collection of self-care ideas and inspiring words contains the pick-me-up you need.

CALM FOR EVERY DAY

Hardback

978-1-80007-182-7

Find calm with this little book. With simple but effective tips to help you manage your emotions and think clearly – including advice on recognizing stress in your body, dealing with anxiety in the moment, mindfulness exercises and self-care ideas – this book will be your guide to staying calm and feeling good.

Have you enjoyed this book?
If so, find us on Facebook at
Summersdale Publishers, on Twitter
at **@Summersdale** and on Instagram
at **@summersdalebooks** and get in
touch. We'd love to hear from you!

www.summersdale.com

Image Credits

Plant illustrations throughout © Uzorchik/Shutterstock.com
pp.3, 48, 117, 157 © Skorik Ekaterina/Shutterstock.com
pp.6, 49, 76, 95, 123, 148 © Tasiania/Shutterstock.com
pp.12, 18, 34, 44, 61, 65, 71, 73, 86, 98, 136, 141 (tree
illustration) © StocKNick/Shutterstock.com
pp.19, 68, 139 © Jane_Mori/Shutterstock.com
pp.5, 64, 113, 122 (cup illustration) © Irina Vaneeva/Shutterstock.com